Daniel
in the
Lions' Den

This book belongs to:

_____

NorthParadePublishing

King Darius of Babylon appointed one hundred and twenty people to help him rule his kingdom.

From those one hundred and twenty people, King Darius chose Daniel and two others to be in charge.

What would King Darius have sat on in his palace? Find the stickers.

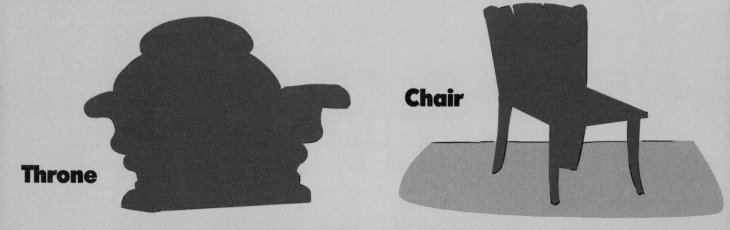

Throne

Chair

King Darius was so impressed with Daniel's good nature and his hard working spirit, that he decided to put Daniel in charge of the whole kingdom.

Stool

Bench

The other servants soon became jealous of Daniel. They knew how much the King liked him and this angered them.

One day they decided to try and find something to get Daniel in trouble, so that the King would get rid of him. However they could not find anything, as Daniel was a good man and obeyed God.

These are some of the good things Daniel did... Find the stickers.

He prayed.

Finally the other servants decided that the only way they could get Daniel into trouble, was to make the king pass a new law. The new law would mean that people were only allowed to worship the King and no other.

He worked hard.

He helped others.

The servants went to the King and told them about their new law. The King liked the idea of everyone praying to him. He asked if everyone had agreed and the servants lied and said, yes. So the law was passed.

The servants then watched Daniel in his house. Daniel knew they were watching, but prayed to his God three times that day as usual.

Daniel prayed to his God three times that day. Find the sticker.

Once in the morning.

After seeing Daniel praying, the servants went straight to King Darius and told him that Daniel was disobeying the law and was praying to his own God.

Once in the afternoon.

And once at nighttime.

The King was very sad when he heard this news. He liked Daniel very much. He tried to change the law so that Daniel would not have to be punished.

The servants went to the King and reminded him that the law could not be changed and that Daniel must be punished for breaking the law. King Darius had no choice but to have Daniel arrested.

Lions can be quite scary. Can you find the stickers of these other scary animals?

Snake

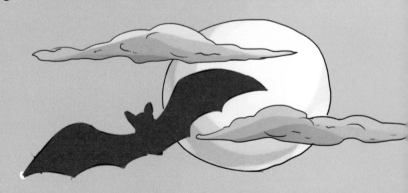

Bat

King Darius sadly gave the order for Daniel to be thrown into the lions' den. The servants happily picked Daniel up and threw him into the den where the lions were waiting.

Spider

Crocodile

A large heavy stone was rolled over the top of the den. As it was being rolled across, the King shouted down to Daniel, "I hope the God to whom you serve and pray, will rescue you."

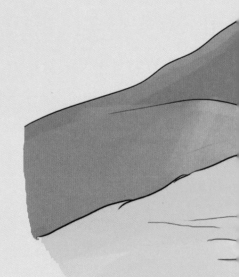

The King returned to his palace, but that night he could not eat anything at dinner. Nor could he sleep throughout the night. He was so worried for poor Daniel in the lions' den.

Lions

Sheep

What animal do some people count to help them get to sleep? Find the stickers.

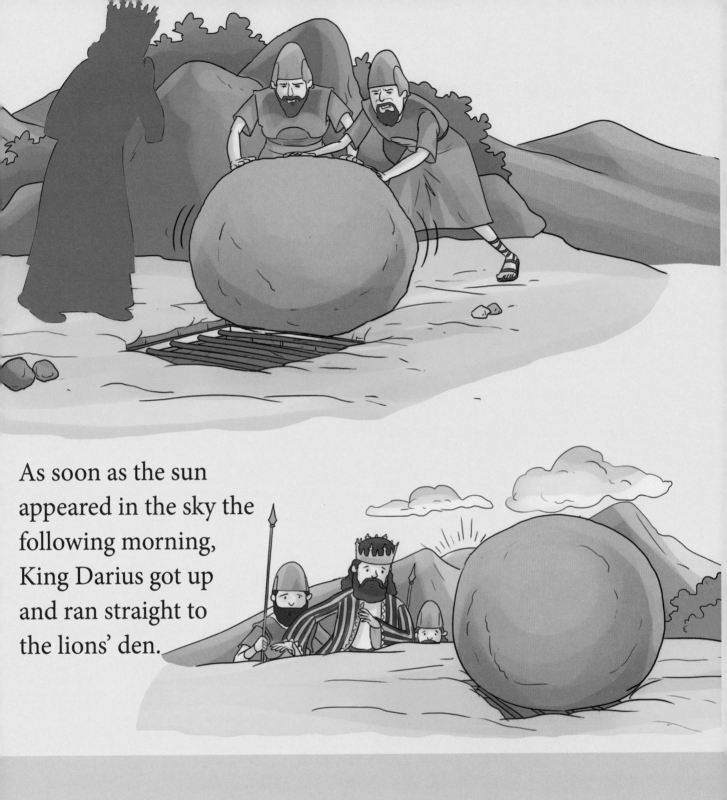

As soon as the sun appeared in the sky the following morning, King Darius got up and ran straight to the lions' den.

Cats

Dogs

As King Darius got closer to the den he shouted to Daniel, "Daniel has your God, to whom you serve and pray, protected you from the lions?"

There was silence for a long period of time, King Darius feared that the lions had eaten poor Daniel.

Can you count how many lions there were in the den?

Can you find all the stickers?

Then suddenly, King Darius heard Daniel's voice from inside the den. "O King, my God sent an angel to shut the mouths of the lions so they could not harm me. He knows I have done no wrong."

King Darius was so delighted that Daniel was safe. He immediately ordered for the stone to be lifted and for Daniel to be released.

King Darius heard that the other servants had tricked him into putting Daniel in the den in the first place. He was very angry and ordered them to be thrown into the den with the lions instead.

From that day on, everyone prayed to Daniel's God. Find the stickers.

After this, King Darius passed a new law. He ordered that everyone in his kingdom must respect the Lord God, who protected Daniel from the hungry lions.